SCHOOL YEAR

by F. Isabel Campoy
Illustrated by Sandra Schaad Mack

Harcourt

Orlando   Boston   Dallas   Chicago   San Diego

Visit *The Learning Site!*

www.harcourtschool.com

My name is Juan. Six months ago, my family and I moved to the United States. At first I had no friends because I didn't speak English. I missed my friends in Mexico.

2

Everything in the United States was so different! The neighborhood was different. The food was different. The school rules were different. Of course, the language was different. I tried hard to learn English so I could make new friends.

On my first day of school, I was
nervous and excited. The kids in my
class smiled at me, but I couldn't
understand what they were saying. My
teacher, Miss Benítez, introduced me to
a boy named Tomás. Tomás speaks
Spanish. He became my first American
friend.

Tomás started helping me learn English right away. At first he had to translate everything for me. Now I understand so much! I am learning more every day.

When I found out that there was a soccer team at school, I was so happy. Soccer is my favorite sport! Mami and Papi said I could join the team. We are the Rockets, and there are boys and girls on the team. Tomás is on the team, too.

I met another good friend playing
soccer. His name is Gan. His family
moved here from Vietnam two years
ago. Gan tells me things he has learned
about fitting in here. I'm learning a lot
from Gan.

One day in March, our class went on
a field trip to the science museum. We
got on the school bus and rode through
the city. It took half an hour to get to
the museum. Everyone was excited!

At the museum, we had to stay together so we wouldn't get lost. A woman took us on a tour. She showed us the dinosaur exhibit first. We saw dinosaur skeletons that were bigger than our school bus! I couldn't wait to tell Mami and Papi about all I'd seen.

In April my class put on a play called *Stone Soup.* When Miss Benítez first told us about the play, I said I wanted to be in it. Then I was afraid that my English wasn't good enough. Miss Benítez said she knew I could do it. Tomás helped me memorize my lines. I was one of the three clever men in the play who make soup from a stone.

We performed our play for our parents and the whole third grade. I was nervous, but I remembered all my lines. At the end, everyone clapped so hard! We bowed and bowed until they stopped. Papi took lots of pictures. I sent some of the pictures to my cousins in Mexico.

I turned nine on May 2. Mami said I
could invite everyone in my class to my
birthday party. We had the party in our
backyard. There was a big piñata shaped
like a dinosaur. It was full of candy!

We ate cake and ice cream. We played musical chairs. We sang songs. Then I opened my gifts and said "Thank you" to all my friends.

Now the school year is almost over. Miss Benítez has asked each of us to give a speech. She told us to choose a topic that interested us. Our speech could be about something new we had learned in science or social studies.

It could be about a famous person
we had learned about. It could be about
an adventure we had had. I thought
and thought. What should my speech
be about?

I know! I will make my speech about my first six months in the United States. I will tell my classmates about the new things I've learned and the new friends I've made. It hasn't always been easy, but it has been fun!